Another Very First Poetry Book

compiled by John Foster

Oxford University Press 1992

Oxford University Press, Walton Street, Oxford OX2 6DP

Oxford New York Toronto
Delhi Bombay Calcutta Madras Karachi
Petaling Jaya Singapore Hong Kong Tokyo
Nairobi Dar es Salaam Cape Town
Melbourne Auckland

and associated companies in
Berlin Ibadan

Oxford is a trade mark of Oxford University Press

Illustrations by Jane Bottomley, Jenny Camons, Frances Cony, Jan Lewis, Alan Marks, Jane Smith.

also in this series:
A Very First Poetry Book
A First Poetry Book
A Second Poetry Book
A Third Poetry Book
A Fourth Poetry Book
A Fifth Poetry Book
A Scottish Poetry Book
A Second Scottish Poetry Book
Another First Poetry Book
Another Second Poetry Book
Another Third Poetry Book
Another Fourth Poetry Book
Another Fifth Poetry Book

ISBN 0 19 917208 0 (hardback)
ISBN 0 19 917209 9 (paperback)

Pentacor PLC, High Wycombe, Bucks
Printed in Hong Kong

Contents

Wiggly Giggles

I've got the wiggly-wiggles today,
And I just can't sit still.
My teacher says she'll have to find
A stop-me-wiggle pill.

I've got the giggly-giggles today;
I couldn't tell you why.
But if Mary hiccups one more time
I'll giggle till I cry.

I've got to stamp my wiggles out
And hold my giggles in,
Cause wiggling makes me giggle
And gigglers never win.

Stacy Jo Crossen
and Natalie Anne Covell

Tiptoe

Yesterday I skipped all day,
The day before I ran,
Today I'm going to tiptoe
Everywhere I can.
I'll tiptoe down the stairway.
I'll tiptoe through the door.
I'll tiptoe to the living room
And give an awful roar
And my father, who is reading,
Will jump up from his chair
And mumble something silly like
'I didn't see you there.'

I'll tiptoe to my mother
And give a little cough
And when she spins to see me
Why, I'll softly tiptoe off.
I'll tiptoe through the meadows,
Over hills and yellow sands
And when my toes get tired
Then I'll tiptoe on my hands.

Karla Kuskin

This morning my dad shouted

This morning my dad shouted.
This morning my dad swore.
There was water through the ceiling
There was water on the floor.
There was water on the carpets.
There was water down the stairs.
The kitchen stools were floating
So were the dining chairs.

This morning I've been crying.
Dad made me so upset.
He shouted and he swore at me
Just 'cause things got so wet.
I only turned the tap on
To get myself a drink.
The trouble is I didn't see
The plug was in the sink.

John Foster

Water's for . . .

Water's for . . .   washing, drinking
             making tea,
             cleaning the bath
             or scrubbing me;
             shining a car
             or rinsing a shirt
             watering tomatoes,
             shifting the dirt
                     . . . my Mum says.

But I say . . .   paddling in wellies
             or just in feet
             (puddles are good
             but sea's a treat)
             squirting at brothers,
             splashing Dad,
             soaking my sister
             to make her mad!
             Mixing with mud
             to bake a pie,
             spraying the dog
             or catching a fly.
             Bath or puddle,
             sleet or rain,
             let's all play
             a WATER game!

Judith Nicholls

All wet

Tommy had a water gun.
He squirted it at Jimmy,
at Jamey, George, and Jennifer,
and Katie, Kim and Timmy.
He squirted Sally on the nose.
He squirted Molly on the toes.
He laughed and thought it
lots of fun
till –
Sammy got him
with the hose.

Tony Johnston

Mandy likes the mud

Polly likes to play with toys
Melissa makes a lot of noise
Ann has a bike
Trevor a trike
But Mandy likes the mud.
She jumps in it
She slumps in it
She scoops it in her hands
She rides on it
She slides on it
She digs to foreign lands.

Kevin likes to kick a ball
Peter never plays at all
Tina cooks tarts
Donna plays darts
But Mandy loves the mud.
She galumphs in it
She splarges
She glugs and slurps and slops
She grins in it
She swims in it
She does smacking belly flops.

Tricia talks to her teddy bear
Belinda combs her doll's long hair
Tracy plays tennis
Mark is a menace
But Mandy adores the mud.

She dives in it

She thrives in it

She paints it on the wall.

Gareth Owen

Jumper

I like to jump into the sky,
I like to jump on springs,
I like to jump on trampolines
And beds that let out pings.

I like to jump from rock to rock,
I like to jump in seas,
I like to jump in muddy pools
That splash up to my knees.

I like to jump onto my hands,
I like to jump up high,
I like to jump and wave my arms
And yell, 'Hello! Goodbye!'

I like to jump in puddings,
I like to jump in jam,
I like to jump in fresh-whipped cream
Exactly as I am.

I like to jump as high as weeds,
I like to jump in strides,
I like to jump and shake up all
The food in my insides

And even in my bed at night
I jump inside my dreams,
Up to the moon and even Mars
And Jupiter it seems.

My bedclothes like to jump as well,
They jump into the air,
They jump onto the floor and then
They land across my chair.

And when the sun begins to rise
I jump into my jeans,
And start my jumping day again
With all my jumping beans.

Michelle Magorian

Three-hole

Three-hole
is the name
of a marble game
we got in Guyana.

Is fun to play
and not hard.
Just dig three lil holes
in you yard
or the sand
by you gate.
Then aim straight

for first-hole

second-hole

18

third-hole

If you lucky
and you marble
go in all the holes
one two three

Then is you chance
to knock you friend marble.
Send it flying for a dance.
When marble burst then fun start.

John Agard

19

Skipping song

Ann and Belinda
Turning the rope
Helen jumps in
But she hasn't got a hope
Helen Freckles
What will you do
Skip on the table
In the Irish stew
Freckles on her face
Freckles on her nose
Freckles on her bum
Freckles on her toes
Helen Freckles
Tell me true
How many freckles
Have you got on you
One two three four five six seven
And out goes you.

Stella Starwars
Skip in soon
Into your spaceship
And off to the moon
Skip on the pavement
One and two
Skip like a rabbit
Or a kangaroo
Skip so high
You never come down
Over the steeples
Over the town
Skip over rooftops
Skip over trees
Skip over rivers
Skip over seas
Skip over London
Skip over Rome
Skip all night
And never come home
Skip over moonbeams
Skip over Mars
Skip through the Milky Way
And try to count the stars
One two three four five six seven
Out goes you.

Gareth Owen

My roller skates

My roller skates won't ever do
The simple things I want them to.
I put them on and try my best.
But one goes East and the other goes West.

I often fall upon the floor.
I stand up and I try once more.
But my roller skates think they know best:
One still goes East and the other goes West.

Finola Akister

Skipping rope

red and orange and violet and green
the rainbow's the brightest skipping-rope
that I have ever seen

Jacqueline Brown

Rainbow chasers

They went to find the rainbow's end:
'It's just a field away!
Please let us go. We promise
We'll be back by end of play.'

The teacher smiled, said, 'Actually,
It's raindrops in the sky.
You'll find it doesn't come to earth.
Still, you could go and try.'

They went to find the rainbow's end,
Quite certain that they could:
'No, not this field, the next one though!
It's just inside the wood.'

And so it was, and so it was,
A warm, calm floor of light;
They stepped into its radiance
And danced from sheer delight.

They went to find the rainbow's end
Deep in a woodland glade;
Saw colours never seen before,
Then watched them slowly fade.

When they came back the teacher teased
'Well, what's the treasure worth?'
Serene, wide-eyed, a child replied,
'This time it came to earth.'

Eric Finney

Storm trouble

The rain
       pops
          drops,
Out of spongy clouds.
As,
the wind
       whirls,
          swirls,
Round bony fingered trees.
And
the lightning
       clashes
          flashes,
Across a frightened face of sky.
While,
the storm
       thunders
          blunders,
In its search for somewhere to hang,
Its dark cloak of weathery trouble.

Ian Souter

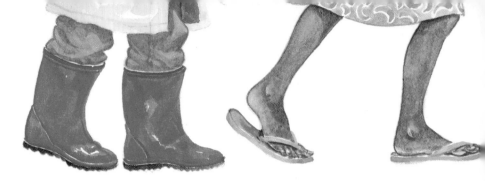

Street sounds

I love to hear my feet
as they're walking down the street
in wellies.
Blobble blabble blobble blabble
wobbly wellie feet.

I like to hear Jane's feet
when she's running down the street
in flip-flops.
Slit-slap, slit-slap
slittery slappery feet.

Listen to Mum's feet
parade along the street
in high heels.
Clock clop clock clop
swanky cloppy feet.

Hear my Grandma's feet
as she shuffles down the street
in slippers.
Shlur plock shlur plock
snorey slippery feet.

Jacqueline Brown

29

Bananas and cream

Bananas and cream,
Bananas and cream:
All we could say was
Bananas and cream.

We couldn't say fruit,
We wouldn't say cow,
We didn't say sugar –
We don't say it now.

Bananas and cream,
Bananas and cream,
All we could shout was
Bananas and cream.

We didn't say why,
We didn't say how;
We forgot it was fruit,
We forgot the old cow;
We *never* said sugar,
We only said *WOW!*

*Bananas and cream,
Bananas and cream;
All that we want is
Bananas and cream!*

We didn't say dish,
We didn't say spoon;
We said not tomorrow,
But *NOW* and *HOW SOON!*

Bananas and cream,
Bananas and cream?
We yelled for bananas,
Bananas and scream!

David McCord

31

Ice lolly

Red rocket
on a stick.
If it shines,
lick it quick.

Round the edges,
on the top,
round the bottom,
do not stop.

Suck the lolly.
lick your lips.
Lick the sides
as it drips

off the stick –
quick, quick,
lick, lick –
Red rocket
on a stick.

Pie Corbett

Snow-cone

Snow-cone nice
Snow-cone sweet
Snow-cone is crush ice
and good for the heat.

When sun really hot
and I thirsty a lot,
Me alone,
Yes me alone,
could eat ten snow-cone.
If you think is lie I tell

wait till you hear the snow-cone bell,
wait till you hear the snow-cone bell.

John Agard

Enough

I've eaten all my vegetables.
Do I have to eat my meat?
I'm strong enough already.
Can't I get down from my seat?

I have eaten all my cabbage.
I have eaten every pea.
I have eaten my potatoes.
There's no room left in me.

I've already grown some muscles –
I'm as fat as any tree.
So do I have to eat my meat
When I'm tall enough for me?

Michelle Magorian

34

Pickled onion!

Pick a pickle
peel a pickle
pop it in a jar . . .
Salt, soak,
seal a pickle
with its vinegar . . .

Pick a pickle
stick a pickle
with a lump of cheese . . .
Sniff, suck,
peck a pickle,
have another?

PLEASE!

Judith Nicholls

Don't tell!

There are lots of things
They won't let me do –
I'm not big enough yet,
They say.
So I patiently wait
Till I'm all grown-up
And I'll show Them all,
One day.
I could show Them now
If They gave me the chance.
There are things I could do
If I tried.
But nobody knows,
No nobody knows, that I'm
Really a giant,
Inside.

Irene Yates

High, there!

A girl next to us who's called Paula
Grew taller and taller and taller;
     When friends called out '*Hi!*'
     She kept wondering why
They looked smaller and smaller and smaller.

David Bateson

The giant's accidents

The giant stood up and hit his head:
he gasped and fell back on the bed.

The bed broke with a mighty crack –
he dropped right through and bumped his back.

He leapt up with a mighty roar
and knocked his elbow on the door.

He stiffened with the sudden pain,
and then he hit his head again.

He staggered round – the room was reeling –
he slipped and crashed straight through the ceiling.

To try to stop his sudden fall
he stretched his arm to grasp the wall.

The noise was heard all over town:
the whole house swayed and tumbled down.

He tunnelled up from underneath
with bits of floorboards in his teeth.

He shook his beard: some bricks dropped out
and gave his toes a nasty clout.

'It can't get worse', he gave a grin,
then slipped on a banana skin.

Charles Thomson

What the giant had for dinner

First
He ate
A hive of bees.

Next
He ate
Some chestnut trees

Then
He ate
A house near me

Last
Of all
He drank the sea.

Ian McMillan and Martyn Wiley

Dinosaur

Who's that knocking
at my door?
Can it be
a dinosaur?

Dinosaurs
are huge and grand
leaving footprints
on the land

As big as anything
can be.
I hope he isn't
after me!

I hope he isn't
looking out
for juicy children
left about . . .

Or nosing round
to find a treat
of something extra
nice to eat.

I hope he hasn't
come to stay.
Dinosaur!
Please go away!

Jean Kenward

Lion

YOU may say
   it isn't true
that a lion's
   close to you,
but I'm certain
   he is there
GROWLING, underneath
   your chair!

YOU may think
   it isn't so.
But I tell you
   that I KNOW
there's a lion
   roaming free
ROARING . . . . Yes.
   The lion's me.

Jean Kenward

41

A Lazy Beast

The African hippopotamus
is very rarely known to fuss,
but loafs in rivers all day long
humming a lazy sort of song.
And when he needs a place to rest
he knows a bed of mud is best.

Michael Dugan

Be impolite

Don't waste your smile
on a crocodile,
for though his grin is wide
you will find
what's on his mind
is, will you come inside?

Michael Dugan

At the dragon-infant school

Dragon-infants
Hang their coats on dragon-pegs
And sit on a dragon-mat
In the corner
To have their dragon-names called out.
The dragon-teacher says
'Now then, little dragons, today
We'll have a story about children!'

44

And the little dragons chuckle
Because they don't
Believe in children.
Sometimes they dress up
In the dragon play-house
And have little dragon-squabbles
Which the dragon-teacher has to sort out
They learn
Lots of dragon-games
And sing dragon-songs
And if they tumble over
In the dragon-playground
They cry dragon-tears
Till Mum comes
To take them home.

Irene Yates

Dragon

On our holiday
   Tom and I
saw a dragon
   in the sky –
and we watched him
   in his flight
upward . . . almost
   out of sight.

How he soared
   and leaped, and leant
over the meadow
   where we went,
while his tail –
   long and slim –
swirled and circled
   under him!

We saw a dragon.
   'Look!' we cried.
Suddenly
   he drooped, and died . . .
There was a stillness.
   Who could tell
he'd be paper
   when he fell?

Jean Kenward

The Windmill

The blades of my windmill are pinned
Onto a stick and spin in the wind,

Turning so quickly through the air
It's hard to tell how many are there,

Quick as the hand of a conjuror
Or the blades of a helicopter.

It's someone with red and yellow arms
Waving them madly in alarm.

Whenever the wind doesn't blow
I run to make my windmill go.

It turns faster the faster I run
And I run faster than anyone.

The windmill makes a lovely
Its colours mix in an orange bl

If I'm tired I stick it in the ground
To wait for a breeze to turn it round.

Stanley Cook

47

Wind Ways

Can you *see* the wind?
No; but he is there,
bending, brushing, smoothing grass,
combing earth's wild hair.

Can you *hear* the wind?
Yes; he pants through trees;
whispers, whines beneath your door:
Can I come in, please?

Can you *smell* the wind?
No; but if you choose,
in his breath you'll smell the smoke
of Autumn barbecues.

Can you *feel* the wind?
Yes; you'll feel his breath
chilling cheeks and chin and lips,
chasing through your teeth.

Can you *taste* the wind?
Only when, on dark December nights,
the chestnut seller roasts his wares
beneath the Christmas lights . . .

Breathe in deeply: you will find
you can almost taste the wind.

Judith Nicholls

Windy day

A wind blew up one morning
And joined us in our play,
Chasing us round the playground
Blowing our ball away.

It whistled at the window
And bustling quickly through
Found our teacher's pile of papers
And blew, and blew, and blew.

Then everybody scrambled
As we heard our teacher shout:
'Quick! Shut the doors and windows
And keep that wild wind out!'

Mary Jeffries

49

Calendar of clothes

January is a time for coats,
for caps and fur-lined boots.

February likes hats with flaps
and zipped-up coloured ski suits.

March can do with anoraks
and jeans and woolly tops.

April needs a change of clothes
for sun and wind and raindrops.

May brings cotton tee-shirts
with jumpers still on hand.

By June the skirts are skimpy,
shorts short for playing on sand.

July comes along in bathing trunks,
and caps with dark green shades.

August gets the sunsuits out
with balls and buckets and spades.

September, and it's back to school,
uniform, shirt and stripey tie.

October brings scarves out again
as leaves whirl up to the sky.

November means turned-up collars
against wind and fog and storm.

December shakes out party frocks.
Christmas fun keeps everyone warm.

Moira Andrew

Baby

Somebody's coming – but we don't know who.
We know it's someone special. We know it's someone new.

We have to wait, although it's here already in a way –
Like something wrapped up underneath the tree on
Christmas day.

We've touched it, felt it move, been close as anybody's been.
We've even heard its heartbeat on a hospital machine –

And yet we don't know anything except it's very small –
That's why we call it 'It' although it's not an 'It' at all!

Granny's hoping for a girl, but we don't really mind.
As long as it behaves itself, we'll play with either kind.

We'll teach it how to clap its hands, and help it hold its cup.
We'll show it where the tadpoles live. We'll watch it
growing up . . .

Somebody's coming – but we don't know when.
Mummy has a feeling in her tummy now and then.

Everything is ready: its room, its clothes, its bed,
The pretty mobile that we made to hang above its head.

Mummy's tired of waiting now. She rests each afternoon.
We know it hasn't far to come: it's bound to be here soon.

One day, when we're out to play, we'll sense that
something's new.
And we'll be so excited that we won't know what to do!

Then Dad will call to us and say, 'Come and meet . . .'

Who?

Paul Rogers

New baby

I like the magic number 3
  the way it used to be,
    when 1 was Mum
      & 2 was Dad
        & 3 was only me.

But 1 is growing fat & round
  & 2 waits at the door
    & 3 is me
      & counting
        to the magic
          number 4.

J. Patrick Lewis

54

Some things don't make any sense at all

My mum says I'm her sugarplum.
My mum says I'm her lamb.
My mum says I'm completely perfect
Just the way I am.
My mum says I'm a super-special wonderful terrific little guy.
My mum just had another baby.
Why?

Judith Viorst

brilliant – like me

today I went with Mum
and Dad on the bus and
the train for our baby

it took us three hours
to travel all that way
but we knew she'd be
worth the long journey

our baby and me are
adopted, but we both
have freckly skin
and I laughed today
when I saw her – she
gave me a gummy grin

I laughed when I saw
her – looking just
like me, she's even got
a funny pointy chin

I'm glad Mum and Dad
chose our baby – I'm
glad they both chose me
it's going to be great
to have a little sister

I think she's brilliant
like me.

Joan Poulson

My terrible sister

My sister is two and she's too much of a baby,
She's always getting in my way.
She makes a lot of noise and breaks my favourite toys,
I wish she'd leave me on my own to play.

My sister is two and she's too much of a nuisance,
She kicks me hard and sometimes pulls my hair.
And when I shout, 'Clear Off!' I'm the one who gets told off –
She gets a hug and kiss, which isn't fair.

My sister is two and she's too too clumsy.
Don't you think it's time she went to bed?
I know it's still the morning, but I'm sure I saw her yawning,
I'll go and get a pillow for her head.

My sister is two but she thinks she is grown up,
She is always wearing boots which are too large.
She's trying to look older but her gumboots trip her over
And she shouts at me and stamps when I'm in charge.

My sister is two and she's too too messy,
She covers all my books with paint and glue.
Mum says it is her age, I'd like to put her in a cage,
My terrible sister who's two.

Michelle Magorian

My brother

My brother is inside the sheet
That gave that awful shout.
I know because those are his feet
So brown and sticking out.

And that's his head that waggles there
And his eyes peeking through –
So I can laugh, so I don't care:
'Ha!' I say. 'It's you.'

Dorothy Aldis

No body

Ghost? That's no ghost,
It's just Susie or Clare
Fooling about
To give us a scare.
Hey, watch me,
Just watch me,
I'll stand on this chair
And whisk off her sheet –
I bet you I dare!
I've done it you see . . .

But there's nobody there.

Eric Finney

Whose is it?

A: This is my one!
   B: No, it's not!
A: It is! It's the one I got!
   B: No, it isn't – look here! See . . .
A: It's the one that was given to me.
   B: It isn't yours: I can show . . .
A: It's mine! It is! I know!
   B: Don't pull – it's not very strong!
A: I want it. I'm right – you're wrong.
   B: It's yours. Look: it's broken in two.
A: It's not mine: it belongs to you.

Charles Thomson

Well, you shouldn't have . . .

Mum – I've just had an explosion.
   Well, you shouldn't have shaken your drink!

Mum – I've just flooded the bathroom.
   Well, you shouldn't have blocked up the sink!

Mum – I've just spilt Grandad's maggots.
   Well, you shouldn't have been in the shed!

Mum – I've just tidied my bedroom.
   Well, you shouldn't have . . . WHAT'S that you said?

Sue Cowling

Coming Home

Mum's been ten days in hospital,
We missed her a lot;
It's seemed more like ten years,
But now guess what?
We've bought a prezzie,
Labelled it:
BEST MUM THERE EVER WAS;
We've cleaned the house
And garden up
Because . . .
              because . . . because . . .

She's coming home,
She's coming home,
SHE'S COMING HOME TODAY!
We're going to treat her
Like a queen.
I hope she'll be O.K.

Eric Finney

64

Rare Bear

My Night Ted got this little hole
It just appeared one day
I said, 'If we ignore it, Ted
It's bound to go away.'
Imagine then my horror when
I next dragged him about
I found that almost all of him
That was inside was out.
I called up M.U.M. for help
'EMERGENCY! IT'S TED!
I think you should come quickly
With your needle and your thread.'
Well, Mum got busy stitching
A hundred's what it took
Or that is what she thought it was
I couldn't bear to look
And when at last she said, 'That's done!'
I didn't dare remark
He hardly seemed like Ted at all
But more like Noah's Ark.

She'd stitched him up and patched and darned
And saved him from the dump
But on the way he'd lost a neck
And gained a camel's hump
His nose was far less nose than snout
His tum was slipping south
There was a kind of penguin look
About his eyes and mouth
I choked, I must apologise
But Mum said, 'There's no need
I think we've prob'ly seen to where
Ignoring holes can lead'
And Ted just blinked as if to say
'It wasn't such a crime.
I wouldn't be this rare new bear
If I'd been stitched in time.'

Hiawyn Oram

Getting undressed

My tie is a snake
coiled up on the mat.
My boxer shorts are
a teddy bear's hat.

My shirt is a ghost –
with a swish and a wail
it lands and lurks
on the curtain rail.

My socks become snowballs.
My sweater's a bird.
My trousers are trunks
of an elephant herd.

That's what I tell
my Mum each day
when she asks me to put
my clothes away.

Jennifer Tweedie

Bathtime

'Brush your teeth
and scrub your knees
and let me see your neck!
Have you washed
behind your ears?
Have you done your back?

'Get the tap on,
here's the soap,
here's the scrubbing brush!
There's dirt
inside that elbow,
let *me* give you a wash!'

Rubbing, scrubbing,
pummelling,
and Dad's as bad as Mum:
'You've got *potatoes*
in your toes
and *paintpots* on your thumb!'

It takes so long
to wash things off,
it really makes me moan.
Maybe next time
I'll speed things up
and do it on my own!

Judith Nicholls

Dark-time

Dark-time, dark-time –
Whispering and . . . 'Hark!' time.
Shadows shifting on the walls.
Ghostly gatherings in the halls.
Fox in the rubbish bin down by the gate.
Slam of a car door, someone home late.
Cat on the prowl. Owl on the wing.
Head under pillow – can't hear a thing.

Dark-time, dark-time –
Whispering and 'Hark!' time,
Rustling and creep-time,
Close my eyes and sleep-time.

Irene Yates

Night lights

My bedroom's at the very top
And when I am in bed
The buses from the street outside
Throw lights above my head.

They glide along my ceiling,
Sometimes fast and sometimes slow,
And I think of all the people
In the bus that's passed below.

And when it's dark and I can't sleep
I lie back and pretend
That every light crossing my room
Is a secret night-time friend.

Michelle Magorian

73

What do you do?

What do you do,
What do you do,
When it's dark
And you need
To go to the loo?

It's warm and snug
As you lie in your bed,
And you think about going
To sleep instead . . .

But deep in your head
A voice keeps saying

Come on! Get up!
You know,
You know,
You can't go to sleep.
You've got to go!

So

What do you do,
What do you do,
When it's dark
And you need
To go to the loo?

You think,
I'm sure that
I don't need to go!
I'm warm and I'm sleepy
The bathroom at night
Is cold and creepy
I'll curl up in bed,
You never know,
That feeling might just go away . . .

But you hear that voice say . . .

Come on! Get up!
You know,
You know,
You can't go to sleep.
You've got to go!

So

What do you do,
What do you do,
When it's dark
And you need
To go to the loo?

You put out a toe
You put out a foot
You put out a leg
It's cold! And so
You find your dressing gown
You threw on the floor

Wrap it round you,
Open the door . . .

And as fast as you can . . .

You go.

David Orme

It's only the storm

'What's that creature that rattles the roof?'
'Hush, it's only the storm.'

'What's blowing the tiles and the branches off?'
'Hush, it's only the storm.'

'What's riding the sky like a wild white horse,
Flashing its teeth and stamping its hooves?'

'Hush, my dear, it's only the storm,
Racing the darkness till it catches the dawn.
Hush, my dear, it's only the storm,
When you wake in the morning, it will be gone.'

Dave Ward

My teddy has a fright

Sometimes my teddy
has a fright
when there's a squeak
or creak at night,
so I cuddle him
and hold him tight,
until he says
he feels alright.

Charles Thomson

The storm

In my bed all safe and warm
I like to listen to the storm.
The thunder rumbles loud and grand –
The rain goes splash and whisper; and
The lightning is so sharp and bright
It sticks its fingers through the night.

Dorothy Aldis

Mornings

If I wake up before it's dawn
And Mum is still asleep,
I sneak barefoot across the hall
To the kitchen where Bud sleeps.

I shush him if he makes a sound,
I tell him not to bark,
And then we creep back to my bed
And snuggle in the dark.

Then I go back to sleep again
With Bud right by my toes,
And wake to find him licking me
And touch his cold, round nose.

And when Mum's clock is ringing loud
And she yells out, 'Wake up!'
I put the tea-bags in the pot,
Pour milk into our cups.

'Hello,' she yawns, her work clothes on,
And Bud jumps up and down.
And then she laughs and fusses him,
Calls him a great big clown.

I like it in the mornings,
Sitting drinking tea,
Watching the sky change colour,
Just Mum and Bud and me.

Michelle Magorian

Cat kisses

Sandpaper kisses
on a cheek or a chin –
that is the way
for a day to begin!

Sandpaper kisses –
a cuddle, a purr.
I have an alarm clock
that's covered with fur.

Bobbi Katz

Cats and dogs

Some like cats, and some like dogs,
and both of course are nice
if cats and dogs are what you want
– but I myself like mice.

For dogs chase cats, and cats chase rats
I guess they think it's fun.
I like my mouse the most because
he won't chase anyone.

N. M. Bodecker

Ocean Travel

If I could travel
the oceans blue,
these are the things
that I would do:

Fly with puffins
under the sea.
Dive with seagulls.
Fish for my tea.

Cling to the tail
of a rolling whale.
Leap with dolphins
in a buffeting gale.

Soar with an eagle.
Hunt with a shark.
Frolick with seals.
Fly home before dark.

Jennifer Tweedie

83

Rainbow socks

If I had new socks
that were striped and bright
I'd put them on my feet,
one left, one right

I'd be glad
if they were magic
and grew wings
to let me fly

I could sit upon
a fluffy cloud,
pick stars
out of the sky

I'd climb onto
a rainbow
to slide down
to the ground

I'd slip in and out
of rainbow stripes
and listen to the music
of rainbow-sound

I'd sing as I slid
in my stripey new socks
and I'd count all the stars
in my rainbow-box

then

whooo – oosh I'd toss them
back up high, speckling
silver stars
into the rainbow-coloured sky.

Joan Poulson

The snowman

He shines like a candle
and melts slowly

He is white and black
and gets smaller all the time

He is as white as feathers
and white horses and snow

He glows in the dark
like a glow-worm

He stands on a flat place
and makes a shadow in the light

He crumples in a circle
like a circus tent

He turns to ice and slush
like a camel's hump

He runs away like milk
and melts like moonlight in sunshine

In the morning he has gone
like the moon.

Gillian Clarke

If I could only take home a snowflake

Snowflakes
like tiny
insects
drifting
down.

Without a hum
they come,
Without a hum
they go.

Snowflakes
like tiny
insects
drifting
down.

If only
I could take
one
home with me
to show
my friends
in the sun,
just for fun,
just for fun.

John Agard

Snow

Ben likes snow when it's first fallen
And there are only birds' feet in it
Em likes snow when it's deep
And she falls in it
And it fills her boots
I like snow when it's icy
And you can slide in it
And toboggan and ride in it
But when it turns to water
And it's just wet
Then we forget
How much we liked it when it was snow

Hiawyn Oram

Snow problem

You can't make friends with a snowman,
So don't give one a cuddle,
Or you'll end up
With a wet shirt front
Standing in a puddle.

John Coldwell

Surprises

Surprises are round
   Or long and tallish.
Surprises are square
   Or flat and smallish.

Surprises are wrapped
   With paper and bow,
And hidden in closets
   Where secrets won't show.

Surprises are often
   Good things to eat;
A get-well toy or
   A birthday treat.

Surprises come
   In such interesting sizes –
I LIKE
   SURPRISES!

Jean Conder Soule

listening

my bike squeaks
and Mum's car clatters

the bus chugs past
and the budgie chatters

if I cover my ears
with my hands
and press down

I can shut all
the sounds out
and be on my own.

Joan Poulson

91

Questions

How far are the stars?
How deep are caves?
Are there men on Mars?
What makes waves?
Why does the tide
Go out and in?
How do tunes come
From a violin?
Why is sky blue?
Where does it end?
What makes a rainbow?
Why does it bend?
Are there really ghosts?
Why does it snow?
So many questions,
So much to know.

Eric Finney

Index of first lines

Acknowledgements

The editor and publisher are grateful for permission to include the following poems.

John Agard, 'Three-Hole', 'Snow-Cone' and 'If I Could Only Take Home a Snowflake' from *I Din Do Nuttin*. Reprinted by permission of The Bodley Head, publishers.   Finola Akister, 'My Roller Skates'. Reprinted by permission of the author.   Dorothy Aldis, 'My Brother' from *Hop Step and Jump* (G P Putnam's Sons) and 'The Storm' from *Everything and Anything*.   Moira Andrew, 'A Calendar of Clothes', © 1992 Moira Andrew. Reprinted by permission of the author.   David Bateson, 'High, There!', © 1992 David Bateson. Reprinted by permission of the author.   N. M. Bodecker, 'Cats and Dogs', from *Snowman Sniffles*. © 1983 N. M. Bodecker. Reprinted by permission of Faber and Faber, Ltd.   Jacqueline Brown, 'Skipping Rope' and 'Street Sounds', both © 1992 Jacqueline Brown. Reprinted by permission of the author.   Gillian Clarke, 'The Snowman' from *There's A Poet Behind You*, ed. M. Styles & H. Cook (A & C Black). Reprinted by permission of the author.   John Coldwell, 'Snow Problem', © 1992 John Coldwell. Reprinted by permission of the author.   Stanley Cook, 'The Windmill', © 1992 Stanley Cook. Reprinted by permission of the author.   Pie Corbett, 'Ice Lolly', © 1992 Pie Corbett. Reprinted by permission of the author.   Sue Cowling, 'Well, You Shouldn't Have . . . '. Reprinted by permission of the author.   Stacy Jo Crossen & Natalie Anne Covell, 'Wiggly Giggles' from *Me Is How I Feel: Poems*. © 1970 by A. Harris Stone, Stacy Crossen, Natalie Covell, Victoria deLarrea. Used by permission of the publisher, Dutton, an imprint of New American Library, a division of Penguin Books USA Inc.   Mary Jeffries, 'Windy Day', © 1992 Mary Jeffries. Reprinted by permission of the author.   Michael Dugan, 'A Lazy Beast', © Michael Dugan. 'Be Impolite' is from Michael Dugan, *Flocks' Socks and Other Shocks* (Penguin, Ringwood, 1989). Both reprinted by permission of the author.   Eric Finney, 'Rainbow Chasers', 'No Body', 'Coming Home' and 'Questions', all © 1992 Eric Finney. Reprinted by permission of the author.   John Foster, 'This Morning My Dad Shouted', © 1992 John Foster. Reprinted by permission of the author.   Tony Johnston, 'All Wet' from *Tomie De Paola's Book of Poems* (Whitebird Inc).   Bobbi Katz, 'Cat Kisses' © 1974 Bobbi Katz. Reprinted by permission of the author.   Jean Kenward, 'Dinosaur', 'Lion' and 'Dragon', © Jean Kenward. Reprinted by permission of the author.   Karla Kuskin, 'Tiptoe' from *Dogs and Dragons, Trees and Dreams* (Harper & Row Publishers, Inc).   J Patrick Lewis, 'New Baby', © J Patrick Lewis. Reprinted by permission of the author.   Michelle Magorian, 'Jumper', 'Enough', 'Night Lights' and 'Mornings' from *Waiting For My Shorts to Dry* (Viking Kestrel, 1989)© Michelle Magorian, 1989. 'My terrible Sister' from *Orange Paw marks* (Viking, 1991) © Michelle Magorian, 1991). Reprinted by permission of Penguin Books Ltd.   David McCord, 'Bananas and Cream' from *One At A Time* © David McCord. Reprinted by permission of the publisher (Little Brown & Co. Inc.)   Ian McMillan & Martyn Wiley, 'What the Giant Had for Dinner', © 1992 Ian McMillan & Martyn Wiley. Reprinted by permission of the authors.   Judith Nicholls, 'Water's For' © 1989 Judith Nicholls, 'Pickled Onion' and 'Wind ways' both © 1992 Judith Nicholls, 'Bathtime' © Judith Nicholls 1988 from *Popcorn Pie* by Judith Nicholls (Mary Glasgow Publications). All reprinted by permission of the author.   Hiawyn Oram, 'Snow' and 'Rare Bear' from *Speaking For Ourselves* (Methuen). Reprinted by permission of Rogers Coleridge & White Ltd.   David Orme, 'What do you do?', © 1992 David Orme. Reprinted by permission of the author.   Gareth Owen, 'Mandy Likes the Mud' and 'Skipping Song' from *Song of the City*. Reprinted by permission of Harper Collins Publishers.   Joan Poulson, 'Brilliant—like me', 'Rainbow Socks' and 'Listening', all © 1992 Joan Poulson. Reprinted by permission of the author.   Paul Rogers, 'Baby'. Reprinted by permission of the author.   Jean Conder Soule, 'Surprises' © Jean Conder Soule. Reprinted by permission of the author.   Ian Souter, 'Storm Trouble', © 1992 Ian Souter. Reprinted by permission of the author.   Charles Thomson, 'The Giant's Accidents', 'Whose Is It?' and 'My Teddy Has a Fright', © 1992 Charles Thomson. Reprinted by permission of the author.   Jennifer Tweedie, 'Getting Undressed' and 'Ocean Travel', © 1992 Jennifer Tweedie. Reprinted by permission of the author.   Judith Viorst, 'Some things don't make any sense at all' from *If I Were in Charge of the World* (Atheneum Publishers Inc). © Judith Viorst. Reprinted by permission of Lescher and Lescher, Ltd.   David Ward, 'It's only the storm', reprinted in *Language in Colour*, ed. Moira Andrew (Belair Publications). Reprinted by permission of the author.   Irene Yates, 'Don't tell!', 'At the dragon-infant school' and 'Dark-time', all © Irene Yates. Reprinted by permission of the author.   Every effort has been made to secure permission prior to printing. However this has not always been possible and the publisher apologizes for any errors or omissions. These will be rectified at the earliest opportunity.